♡ Ch

F

Love: Renée

The First Noel
A Tale of Friendship

by Clare Johnson and Nicole Thomas

Endorsements:

"I whole-heartedly endorse the First Noel. Such a magical telling of the story of Jesus' birth. The poetry flows like a dance within your mind as you go through the incredible imagery. This deserves a spot on your bookshelf and to be read annually. I see this book becoming a tradition within families to read together the story of our savior." **-Brae Wyckoff-Director of *Kingdom Writers Association* and award-winning Amazon bestselling author**

"The First Noel is a Christmas story for all ages. It reminds us of Christ's greatest two commandments, loving God and loving people, while making sure we understand that all are welcome to enter his kingdom, regardless of our differences." **-Theresa Harvard Johnson, Author of *The Scribal Anointing* book series**

From Clare Johnson:

Thank you first and foremost to God, the author of all creativity, for making this book possible. Thank you also to Eric Johnson, my wonderful husband, who supported and encouraged me wholeheartedly with this project. I would also like to give special acknowledgement to Nicole Thomas, owner and artistic director of Dunamix Dance Project, who received this story through a dream and gave me the privilege and honor to collaborate in the writing for the dance production, The First Noel. Lastly, a special thank you to our talented illustrator, Sierra Ghironzi, for all of her hard work.

From Nicole Thomas:

Many thanks to the dancers, costume, set and prop designers, choreographers, parent helpers and staff who generously donated their time and talent to birthing this vision with such incredible excellence. Special thanks to Clare Johnson for working tirelessly with me to write scripts for over four productions now and hopefully many more to come as God continues to guide our paths. Thank you Sierra for your time at Dunamix as a dancer, choreographer and teacher, your delightful illustrations have captured the heart in this beautiful story. I am humbled, and honored by the many miracles that play out all around me. What a gift!

Clare Johnson Bio:

Clare Johnson is a writer, dancer, teacher, and choreographer. Her writings include original dance productions, and songs as well as her blog "Hope in the Making". Her dance productions have been performed at woman's conferences, out reaches, church events, and prisons. Whether creating through writing or dance productions, her desire is to bring a message of hope to others through all of her work. She lives in California with her wonderful husband and children and confesses an affinity for cats of all kinds.

Nicole Thomas Bio:

Nicole Thomas started her dance school in 1999, with a vision to teach dance with integrity. It has grown into what is now Dunamix Dance Project in Southern California. Nicole loves to bring awareness to current social justice issues through dance and the First Noel story came to her as a statement about how much God loves people, and wants them to be treated equally. Nicole is happily married with three beautiful children. She has a cat and a dog and dreams of some day owning a mini pony.

Prologue:

Originally written as a dance production, this Christmas poem weaves the heartwarming fictional tale of a Wiseman's daughter, a poor shepherd girl, and the journey of their friendship into the traditional Biblical account of Jesus' birth. The story begins two thousand years ago, when the two young girls meet for the first time in the Jewish marketplace.

The hub of town, the marketplace,
People gathered of every race;
Rich and poor, every social class,
Traders, merchants, that way would pass.

Wiseman and daughter once a year
Would travel far to purchase here.
She saw her in the marketplace
With tattered clothes and dirt on face.

3

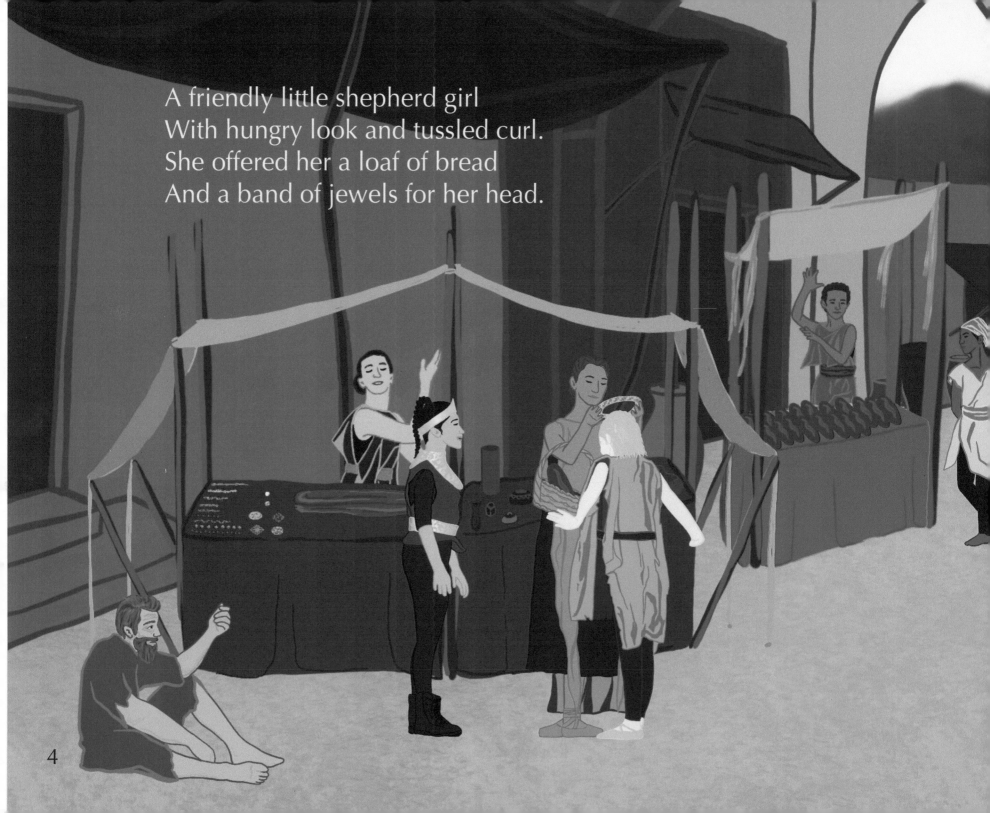

A friendly little shepherd girl
With hungry look and tussled curl.
She offered her a loaf of bread
And a band of jewels for her head.

4

Lack and stature hardly mattered.
As friends do, they played and chattered.

They waved goodbye 'till next they meet,
And vowed their friendship dear and sweet.

5

When next year's trip came about,
The daughter scorned her without
Fine apparel, jewels, or food.
Her prejudice had made her rude.

Head lifted up with hardened pride,
Her change of heart she could not hide.
Surely shepherd girls who are poor,
Should be despised by those with more.

Next year when the girls were older,
Wiseman's girl was even bolder.

She snubbed her nose as she walked past,
Contempt for girl of shepherd's class.
Of course those known for noble birth
Surpass others with little worth.

9

It came to pass the Emperor
Called his people to register.
So all went to their own city.
Joseph went up from Galilee.

10

He traveled far to Bethlehem. Mary, his wife, rode with him. She was pregnant and so tired. A place to rest she desired.

Hustle, bustle, it's getting late.
Busy innkeepers, business great,
Take their money, gather their gold.
"Folks get inside. It's growing cold!"
Weary couple from long roads trod,
Ready to birth the Son of God,

Could find no room at any inn. Each place was filled up to the brim. "I have no room where you can stay. But rather than send you away, Come find shelter in my stable. Receive comfort if you're able".

13

As shepherds watched their flocks by night,
Behold, an angel in their sight!
The glory of the Lord so bright
Gave trembling shepherds awful fright.
The angel said to them, "Do not fear.
I bring you tidings of great cheer!
For born this day in Bethlehem
Is Christ, the Lord, Savior to men.
And to you this will be the sign:
Babe wrapped in swaddling clothes you'll find."

Suddenly, up in starry sky,
A multitude of angels cry,
"Peace on the earth! Goodwill to men!
The Savior's born in Bethlehem!"

Once they heard the announcement,
To Bethlehem the shepherds went.
"Let's see this thing that's come to pass,
Which God made known to shepherds' class!"

They came with haste and found the babe.
Mary and Joseph had Jesus laid,
In a manger, his first bed.
It was just as the angels said.

19

Wisemen from the East travelled far.
Followed God's sign, a shining star.

"Where is he, born King of the Jews?
We've come to give Him worship due."
King Herod heard what Wisemen said.
The news filled his soul with hatred.
"Go and search for the young king
That worship to Him I may bring."

22

Later in an awful dream,
God warned them, of Herod's scheme.
Keep the babe from him they must!
Their route home they would adjust.

Finding the child, great gifts they gave,
Representing king, priest, and grave.
Newborn king, though ruler of all,
Chose not palace, but lowly stall.
As guests to witness humble sight,
He chose high class and low that night.
Savior of shepherd and wiseman,
In His eyes, class didn't define them.

Born to save both rich and poor.
Loved the same by the Savior.
Impacted by so great a grace,
That both classes he would embrace,
Wiseman's daughter humbled her heart
And welcomed friendship, a new start.
Her prejudice had marred her soul
But Jesus' birth had made her whole.

She ran up to the shepherd girl
With tattered clothes and tussled curl.
She shared her heart and mourned the day
She chose to push her friend away.

As friends do, they laughed and chattered
About the things that really mattered.

27

And vowed to live lives that bring
Glory to the newborn king.

"I am giving you a new commandment, that you love one another. Just as I have loved you, so you too are to love one another. " John 13:34

CPSIA information can be obtained
at www.ICGtesting.com
Printed in the USA
BVHW091805061120
592562BV00001B/4